D1400124

Copyright © 1993 by Rod Campbell

This edition published by Barnes & Noble, Inc.,
by arrangement with Macmillan Children's Books,
Macmillan Publishers Ltd, a division of Macmillan Ltd

First published in 1993 by Campbell Books

All rights reserved. No part of this book may be used or reproduced
in any manner whatsoever without the written permission of the Publisher.

1997 Barnes & Noble Books

Printed and bound in Singapare

ISBN 0-7607-0506-2

97 98 99 00 01 M 9 8 7 6 5 4 3 2 1

Our house

Open all the windows,
And don't forget the door,
See Mummy, Daddy, Sue and Sam –
And Rover makes one more!

The weather

The weather's been —

foggy   windy   cloudy

rainy   stormy   snowy

And isn't it funny, today it's

Lost teddy

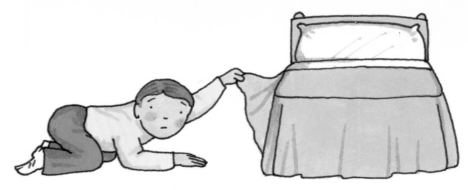

Oh where, oh where is teddy,
My naughty teddy bear?

I've looked and looked for teddy –
I've looked everywhere!

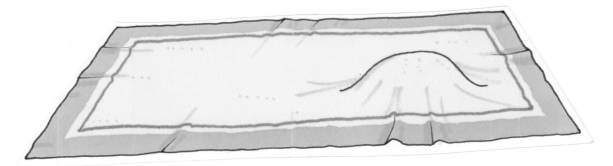

What's that bump in the carpet?
Can that be my bear?
Teddy, teddy, teddy,
Come out from under there!

MY
Lift-the-Flap
NURSERY BOOK

ROD CAMPBELL

BARNES
&NOBLE
BOOKS
NEW YORK

Incy wincy spider

Incy wincy spider
Climbing up the spout.
Down came the rain
And washed the spider out.*

Out came the sunshine
And dried up all the rain;
Incy wincy spider,
Climbing up again.†

*open flap   †close flap

At playschool

Coat on your peg

Meet Jill and Greg

Draw a shy mouse

Then build a house

Go to your seat

Now something to eat!

Baa, baa, black sheep

Baa, baa, black sheep,
Have you any wool?
Yes sir, yes sir,
Three bags full;

One for the master,
One for the dame,
And one for the little boy
Who lives down the lane.

The three brown puppies song

(sing to the tune of 10 Green Bottles)

Three brown puppies
           sitting on a wall,
Three brown puppies
           sitting on a wall,
If one brown puppy
           should accidentally fall,*
There'd be two brown puppies
           sitting on a wall.

*fold a flap over and hold it down

Toy soldiers

The castle's full of soldiers,
Dressed in red and blue;
I can see all seven –
Can you see them too?

Two brown puppies
        sitting on a wall,
Two brown puppies
        sitting on a wall,
If one brown puppy
        should accidentally fall,*
There'd be one brown puppy
        sitting on a wall.

One brown puppy
        sitting on a wall,
One brown puppy
        sitting on a wall,
If one brown puppy
        should accidentally fall,*
There'd be no brown puppies
        sitting on a wall.

Kim's game

Lift the cover from the tray,
And counting one, two, three,
Look at all the objects there,
And remember all you see.

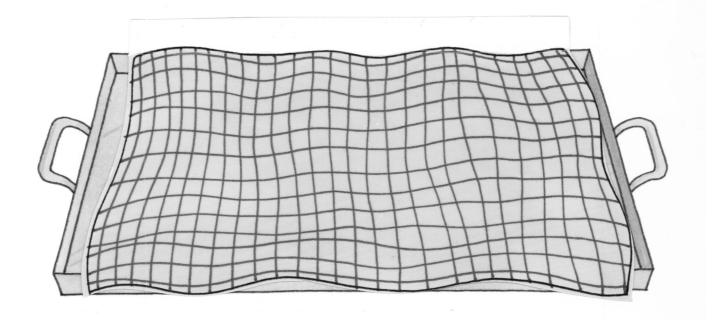

Put the cover gently back,
And now we start the game!
Think of all the things you saw;
How many can you name?

Sing a song of sixpence

Sing a song of sixpence,
A pocket full of rye;
Four and twenty blackbirds
Baked in a pie.

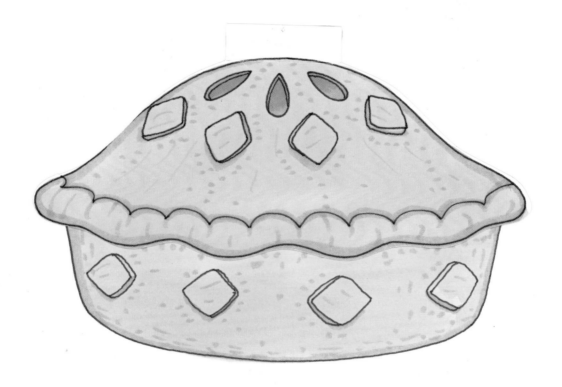

When the pie was opened,
The birds began to sing;
Wasn't that a dainty dish,
To set before the King?

The King was in his counting house,
Counting out his money;
The Queen was in the parlour
Eating bread and honey.

The maid was in the garden
Hanging out the clothes,
When down came a blackbird
And pecked off her nose.

(But Jenny Wren put it back again!)

Creepy crawlies

Little creatures live in trees,
Hiding away under leaves;
Very small and hard to see,
They crawl about, quietly.

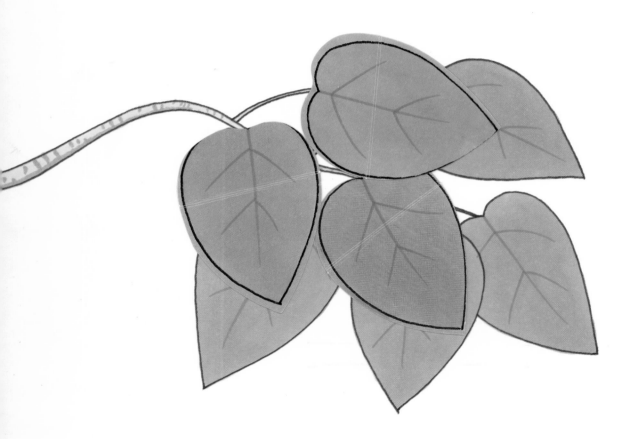

Go on now, lift a leaf –
See what's sitting underneath.

Toy train

Clackety clack,
Clackety clack,
The toy train's chugging
Round the track.

Where are the toys going today?
Over the hills and far away;
To strange lands across the sea,
And home again in time for tea!

The teddybears' picnic

Into the field

Through the wood

Over the log

This place looks good!

The hamper's very heavy
With lots of things to eat;
There's cakes and scones and lemonade –
A special picnic treat!

Pat-a-cake

Pat-a-cake, pat-a-cake, baker's man,
Bake me a cake as fast as you can;

Pat it and prick it and mark it with B,
And put it in the oven for baby and me.

Ring-a-ring o' roses

Ring-a-ring o' roses,
A pocket full of posies,
Atishoo! Atishoo!
We all fall down!

*Stand the children up at the start, and
push them over on reaching the last line.*

Baby animals

Two bouncy puppies
Exactly the same,

Three baby rabbits
Friendly and tame.

Four fluffy chicks
Pecking the ground,

Five sleepy kittens –
Shh, not a sound!

Holiday time

Pack all you'll need
To play with and wear;

bucket and spade

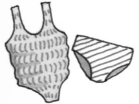
swimsuits

trousers

dress

cap

sunglasses

books

bat and ball

hat

shoes

socks

Open your suitcase –
Is everything there?

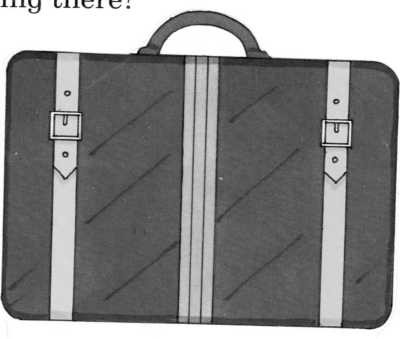

Noah's ark

The animals went in two by two –
Mr Noah's floating zoo.

My plane

Flying in my plane
Is what I like to do;
I'm never on my own –
My fluffy friend comes too!

Goodnight!

Twinkle, twinkle, little star,
How I wonder what you are!
Up above the world so high,
Like a diamond in the sky.

When the great red sun has gone,
When he nothing shines upon,
Then you give your little light,
Twinkle, twinkle, through the night.